Christmas 1943.

MEN, WOMEN AND DOGS

Other books by James Thurber

THE OWL IN THE ATTIC

THE SEAL IN THE BEDROOM

MY LIFE AND HARD TIMES

THE MIDDLE-AGED MAN ON THE FLYING TRAPEZE

LET YOUR MIND ALONE

THE LAST FLOWER

FABLES FOR OUR TIME

MY WORLD—AND WELCOME TO IT

* * *

IS SEX NECESSARY? (with E. B. White)

THE MALE ANIMAL, a Play (with Elliott Nugent)

Thurber's MEN, WOMEN AND DOGS

A BOOK OF DRAWINGS

WITH A PREFACE BY *Dorothy Parker*

HARCOURT, BRACE AND COMPANY, NEW YORK

TO ANDY WHITE

who picked up the first of these
restless scrawls from the floor
fifteen years ago and bravely set
about the considerable task of
getting them published, this book
is gratefully and affectionately
dedicated

ACKNOWLEDGMENT

All the captioned drawings published in this book were first printed in *The New Yorker*. Most of the spots also appeared in the same magazine with the exception of a few drawn especially for this book by James Thurber.

PREFACE

I had long ago made my design for what was to become of me when the Reaper had swung his scythe through my neck. I was to be cremated after death—at least, I always trusted it would be after death. I even left instructions to this effect in my will, a document that might otherwise have been writ in a large, schoolgirl backhand on the head of a pin. Now, with the publication of this book, I must change those words, and with them my plans for the long, long rest. Now I want to be left as approximately is, so I may be buried in a prominent place on a travelled thoroughfare through a wildly popular cemetery. Above me I want a big white stone—you will see why it must be big—on which I want carven in clear letters: "Uncover before this dust, for when it was a woman, it was doubly honored. Twice in life, it was given to her below to introduce the work of James Thurber. Reader, who around here, including you, can tie that record?"

I like to think of my shining tombstone. It gives me, as you might say, something to live for.

It gives me, also, a lovely diversion with which to while away eternity. I have always found it best to be quiet and alone with a Thurber drawing, that I may seek to fathom what went on in the lives of the characters depicted, before the artist chose his moment for setting them down forever. Sometimes I wonder if eternity is going to be half long enough for me to make anything near a reasonable guess.

Consider, for instance, the picture showing a man, his wife, and a male guest. They are standing in a something less than gracious enclosure, furnished mainly with a bookcase apparently ordered by mail from the company that did such notable work in Pisa. And on top of the bookcase is a woman on all fours. So help me God,

vii

there is a woman on all fours on top of the bookcase. And the host is saying, "That's my first wife up there, and this is the *present* Mrs. Harris."

Well, what would you do about that? I worked for a while on the theory that the first Mrs. Harris, the one on top of the bookcase, was dead and stuffed, but my heart was never really in it. In the first place, she doesn't look stuffed; she looks limp. She looks limp and resigned and only a trifle bewildered. She has the look of having been where she is for a long time. How do they feed her? Do they put a cover over her at night? And what made her husband dispose of her and take his present mate? The new spouse is no more sweetly shaped, no more elegantly clothed, no more carefully coiffed than the old one. They look equally terrible. Could it be that the first wife had a habit of crouching on top of book-cases, and one day he could stand it no longer and said, "Oh, all right, if *that's* what you want to do," and flung out and got married again? What does the new wife, that *present* Mrs. Harris, think of the arrangement? She looks not too sensitive, luckily for her, but she must know, when her friends come in for bridge, that her household is not overly conventional. And the bookcase is full of books. What books, in heaven's name, what books do such people read?

You understand what I mean when I say that eternity will not be long enough for my figuring?

Or take again, for instance, the fine drawing of the court scene— the mild judge, the cocksure lawyer, and the aghast witness. "Per-haps *this* will refresh your memory," the lawyer is saying in his nasty way, as he produces, no doubt with a flourish, a kangaroo— a tender, young, innocent, wistful kangaroo. What, I ask you, what can lie back of that?

I give up such things; or at least I say I do. But I find I keep on working at them through the white nights.

I cannot say that James Thurber's work has progressed. No more could I say that the new moon is more exquisite than the last one. I will not be so illiterate as to expand the perfect into the more perfect.

But I do say I see certain changes in his characters. The men seem to me, in the main, a little smaller, even a little more innocent, even a little more willing to please than before. Also, the *pince nez*, superbly done by a slanted line across the nose, seems to be more widely worn by them. It is to be hoped they do not turn to glasses to obtain a better view of their women. Because the ladies are increasingly awful. They get worse and worse, as we sit here. And there they are behaving, with never a moment's doubt, like *femmes fatales*.

It is hard for me to comment on The War Between Men and Women, for naturally I am partisan because of my sex. It is tough going for me to see the women in retreat, routed; finally to witness the woman general, mounted on that curious horse, doubtless a spy, surrendering her baseball bat to the late enemy. I comforted myself with the fact that no man had equaled the strange wild daring of Mrs. Pritchard's Leap. Then I realized I needed no such comfort. For if you study this glorious battle sequence closely, you will realize that the women, rout or no rout, surrender or no surrender, are the real winners. I suppose I understand that we are licked only when I say I doubt if our victory is for the best.

Mr. Thurber's animals have not changed with his new work; they have just got more so. My heart used to grow soft at the sight of his dogs; now it turns completely liquid. I give you, for the third time in instance, that darling who looks cautiously out his door, curves his paw to the snowstorm, and turns his poor, bewildered head up to the spewing heavens. There is nowhere else existent an innocence like to that of Thurber animals. . . . Even that strange, square beast, beside which lie the neat hat, the cold pipe, the empty shoe, and in front of which stands the stern woman, her hands on her hips, demanding, "What have you done with Dr. Millmoss?" . . .

You see how easy it is to say "Thurber animals." The artist has gone into the language. How often we say, "He's a Thurber man" or "Look at that woman—she's a perfect Thurber," and, God help us and them, we are always understood. We need say no more about them. We have been taught to recognize them by the

ix

master. Possibly Thurber humans and animals existed before the artist drew them. I am willing to concede that they may have, but I am strong to say that I doubt it. I believe that Nature again has been shown her place, and has gone into her old specialty of imitating art.

Two of my best friends are dogs of a whirling mélange of ancestry. They are short in the paw, long and wavering in the body, heavy and worried in the head. They are willing, useless, and irresistible. Nobody ever asks their breed. "Oh, look at the Thurber dogs," people say who see them for the first time. . . . If I were Mr. Thurber, I should rather have my name used that way even than have it bracketed, as it has so often been, with that of Matisse. . . .

I think you must know how I feel to be in the same book with a fine artist, to be standing here, this moment and forever, presenting his finest work. That is why I choke a little when I say, and with doubled privilege and doubled pride that I may say it again: Ladies and gentlemen, Mr. James Thurber.

DOROTHY PARKER

New York, 1943

x

CONTENTS

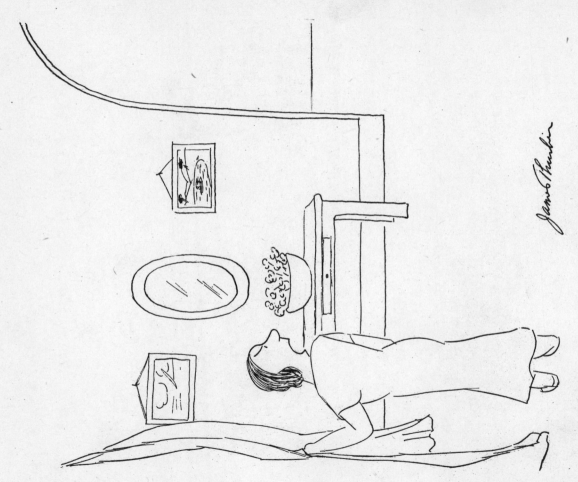

"Well, don't come and look at the rainbow then, you big ape!"

"She has the true Emily Dickinson spirit except that she gets fed up occasionally."

"All right, all right, try it that way! Go ahead and try it that way!"

"They were shot by George's uncle—the one that lost his mind."

James Thurber

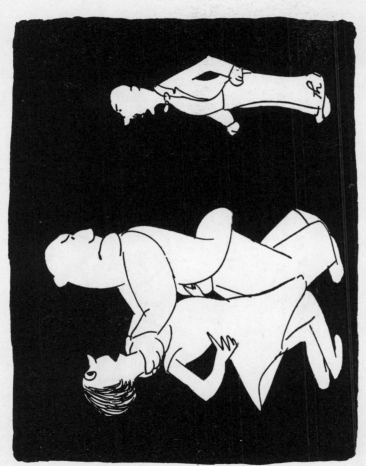

"Have you no code, man?"

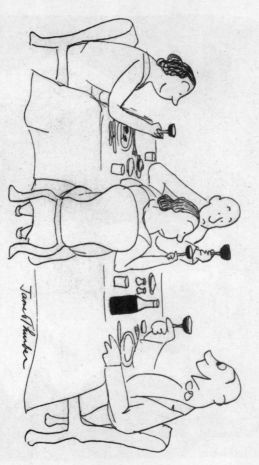

"It's a naïve domestic Burgundy without any breeding, but I think you'll be amused by its presumption."

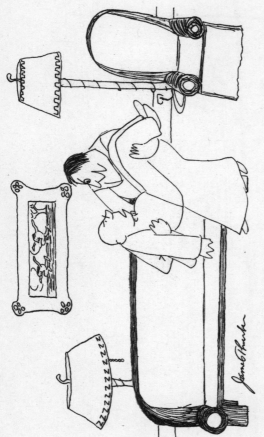

"*You're going a bit far, Miss Blanchard.*"

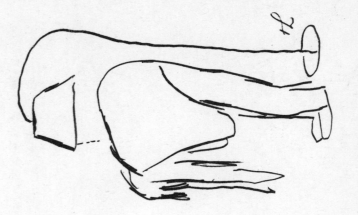

"Bang! Bang! Bang!"

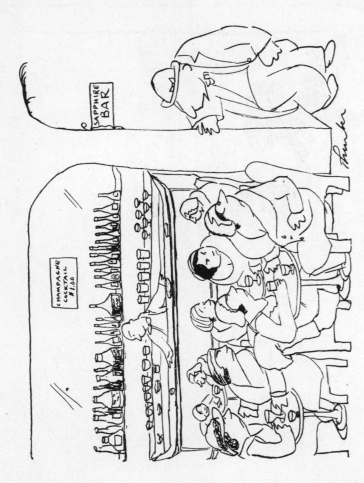

"You gah dam pussy cats!"

"*It's Lida Bascom's husband—he's frightfully unhappy.*"

"What do you want to be inscrutable for, Marcia?"

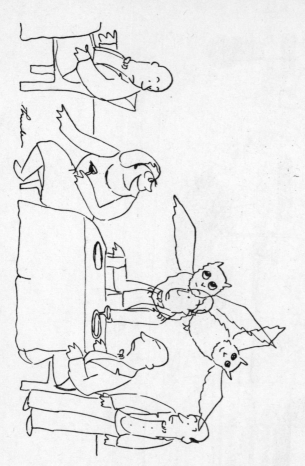

"Look out! Here they come again!"

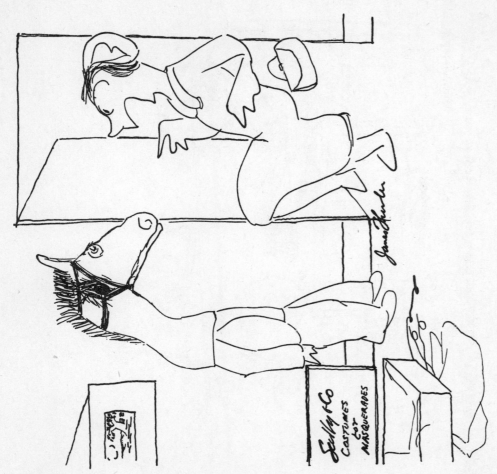

"I'm afraid you are in the wrong apartment, Madam."

"Why do you keep raising me when you _know_ I'm bluffing?"

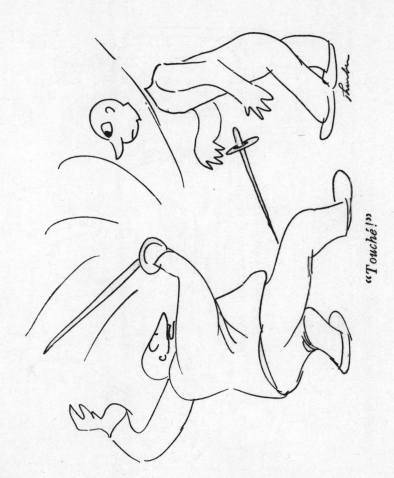

"Touché!"

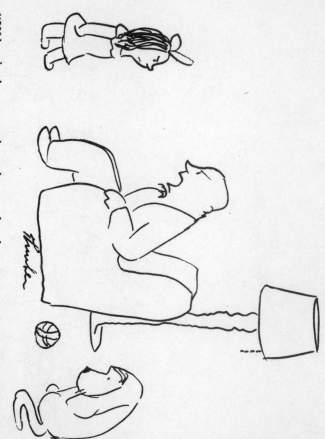

"Why don't you wait and see what becomes of your _own_ generation before you jump on mine?"

"There's no use you trying to save _me_, my good man."

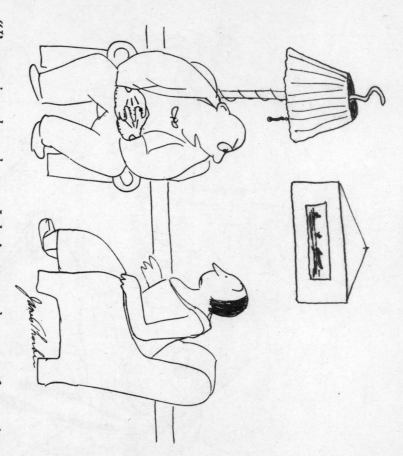

"I'm wearing gloves because I don't want to leave any fingerprints around."

"I come from haunts of coot and hern!"

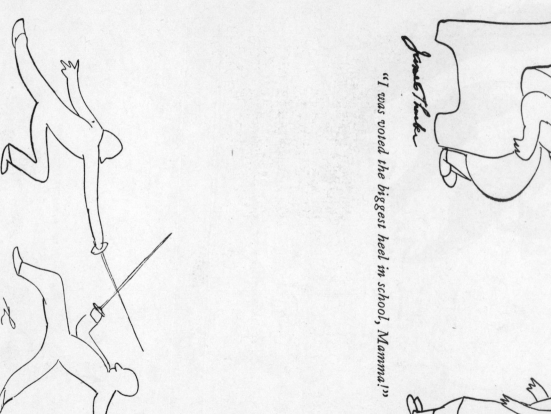

"I was voted the biggest heel in school, Mamma!"

"*You and your premonitions!*"

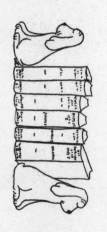

"She's reading some novel that's breaking her heart, but we don't know where she hides it."

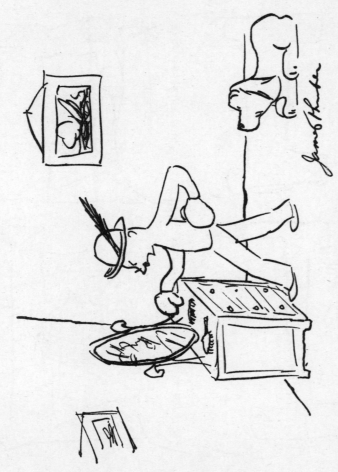

"They're going to put you away if you don't quit acting like this."

"You were wonderful at the Gardners' last night, Fred, when you turned on the charm."

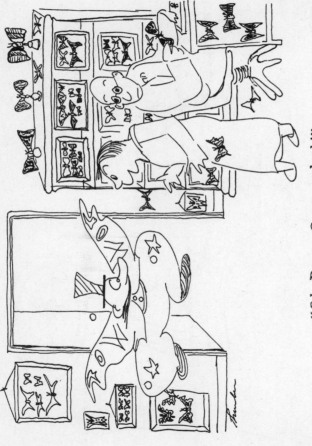

"Oh, Doctor Conroy—look!"

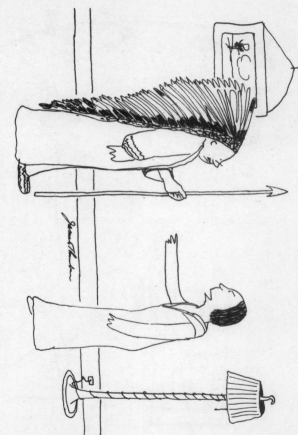

"You haven't got the face for it, for _one_ thing."

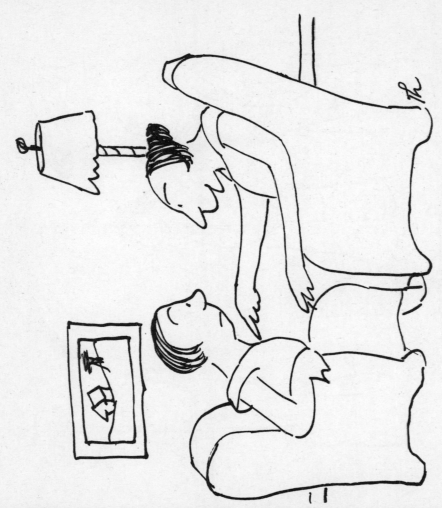

"Of course he's terribly nervous, but I'm sure he meant it as a pass at me."

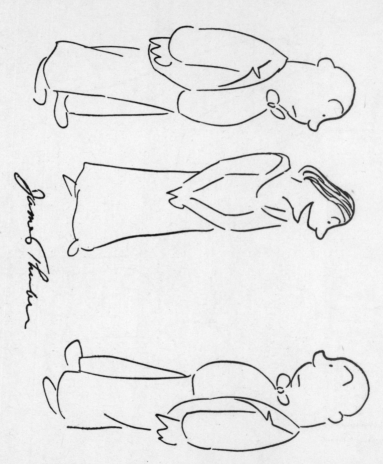

"Well, the bridge game is off. Ely Culbertson is coming and he wants us all to help plan the post-war world."

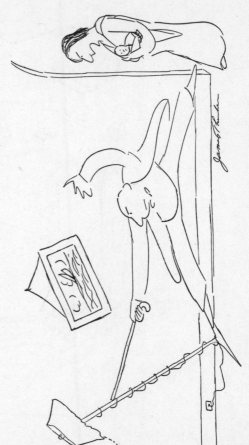

"Who are you today—Ronald Colman?"

"Here! Here! There's a place for that, sir!"

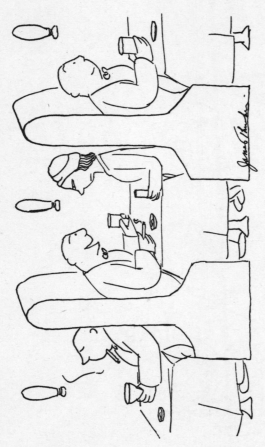

"Maybe you don't have charm, Lily, but you're enigmatic."

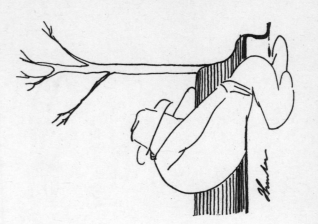

"What have you done with Dr. Millmoss?"

"One of you men in the kitchen give the officer another drink!"

"What do four ones beat?"

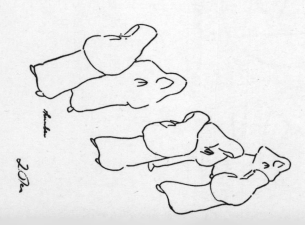

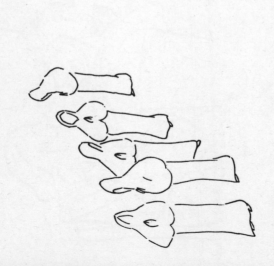

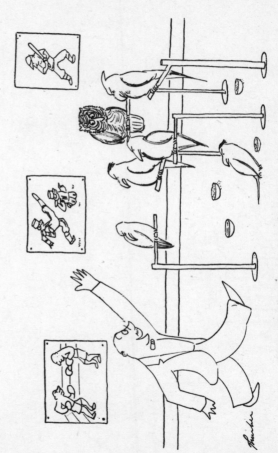

"*Good morning, my feathered friends!*"

"I can't get in touch with your uncle, but there's a horse here that wants to say hello."

"I'm so glad you're a writer—I'm just full of themes and ideas."

"*I drew three more clubs and filled my flush!*"

"You're not my patient, you're my meat, Mrs. Quist!"

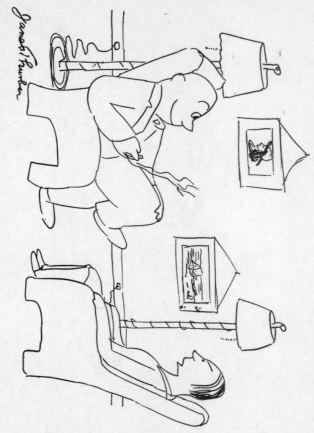

"Why don't you let *me* know what it is, if it's so pleasant?"

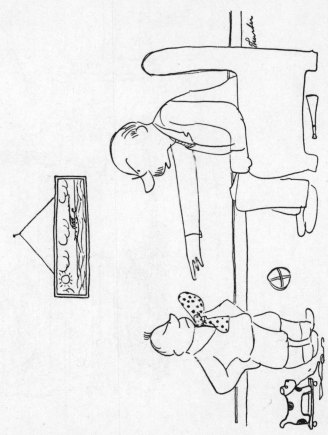

"I'll thank you to keep your mother's name out of this!"

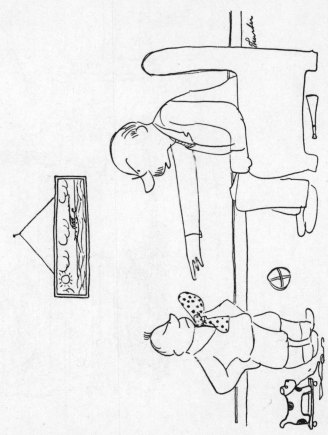

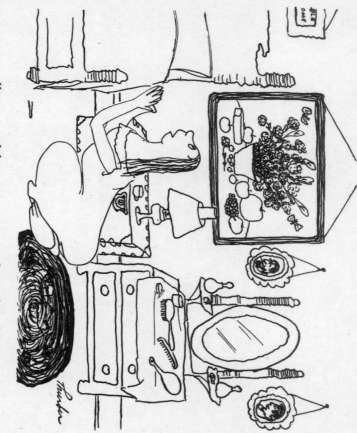

" . . . and keep me a normal, healthy girl."

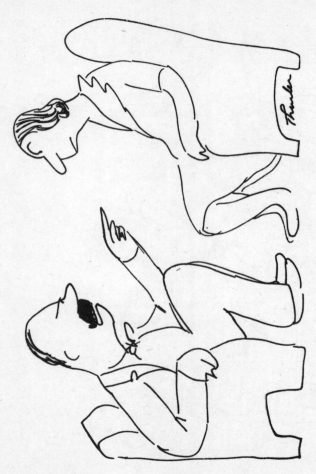

"That martyred look won't get you anywhere with me!"

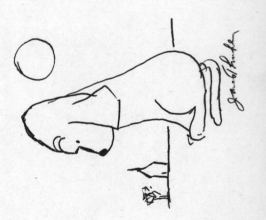

"This is Miss Jones, Doctor—I want you to cheer her up. She's been through hell recently."

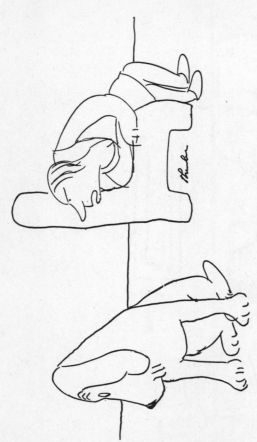

"For Heaven's sake, why don't you go outdoors and trace something?"

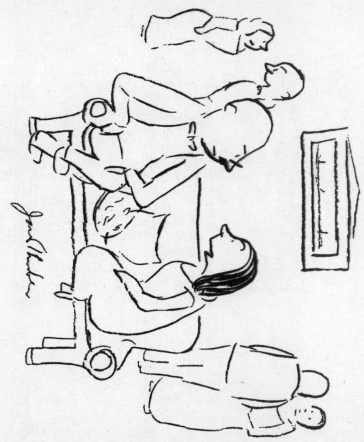

"*I think of you as being enormously alive.*"

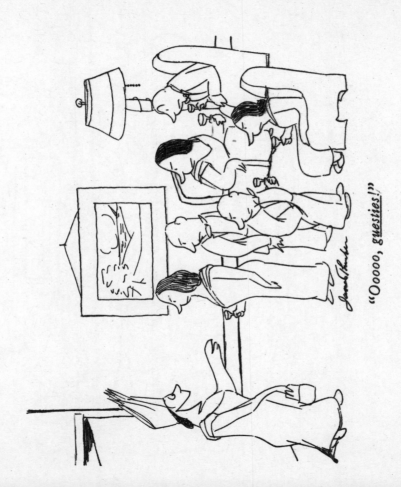

"Ooooo, guesties!"

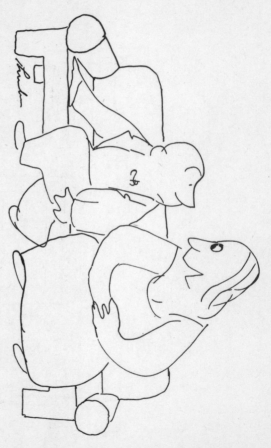

"If you can keep a secret, I'll tell you how my husband died."

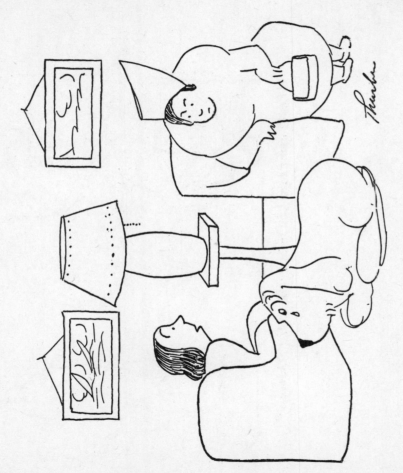

"He's been like this ever since Munich."

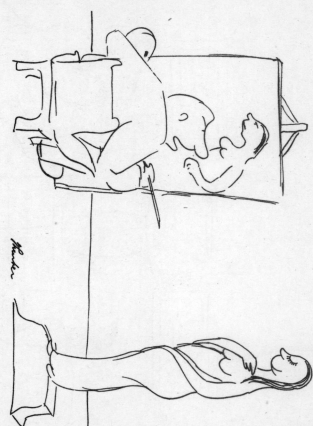

"What's come over you since Friday, Miss Schemke?"

"Here's to m' first wife, darling—she only wore one hat, God bless 'er!"

"The trouble with me is I can never say no."

53

"I'm Virgo with the moon in Aries, if that will help you any."

"There go the most intelligent of all animals."

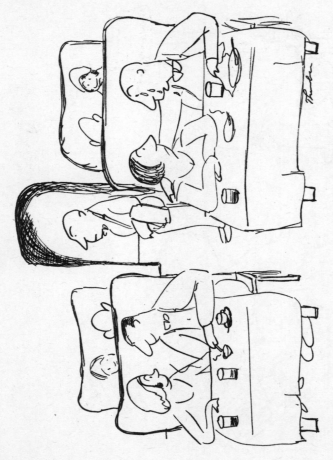

"My wife had me arrested one night last week."

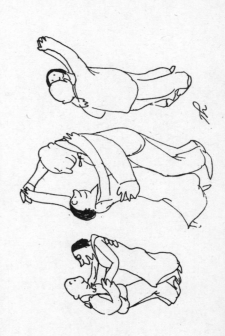

"Why did I ever marry below my emotional level!"

"One of us ought to be a Boswell, taking this all down."

"I'd feel a great deal easier if her husband hadn't gone to bed."

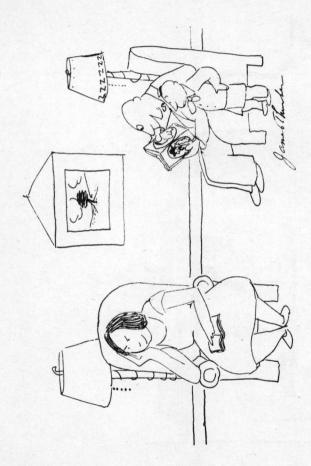

"And this is Tom Weatherby, an old beau of your mother's. He never got to first base."

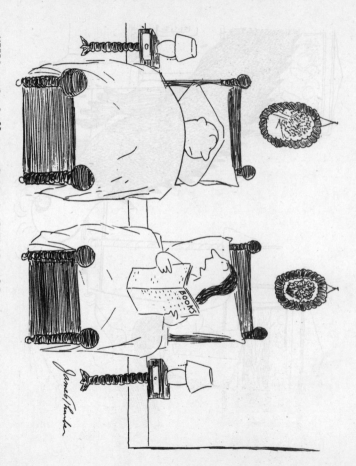

"What the hell ever happened to the old-fashioned love story?"

61

"Shut up, Prince! What's biting you?"

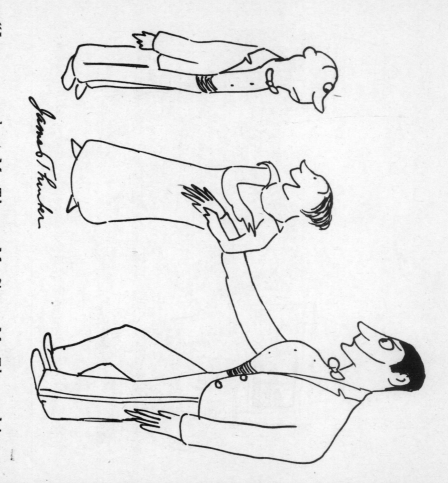

"I want you to know Mr. Thrawn, Mr. Simms. Mr. Thrawn claims to be a werewolf."

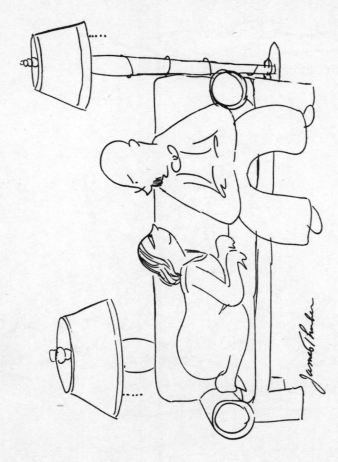

"My heart has been a stick of wood since May, 1927, Miss Prentice."

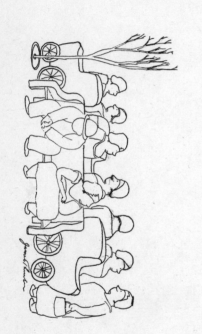

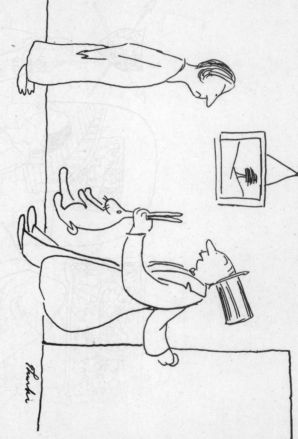

"Darling, I seem to have this rabbit."

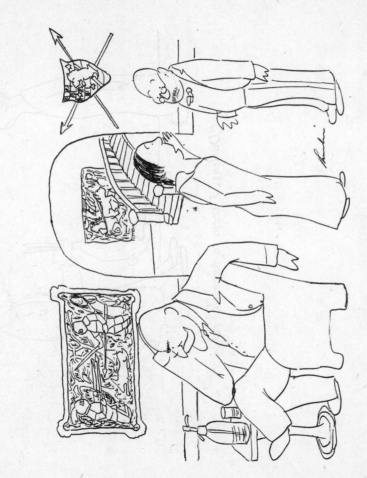

"He's just heard about the changes that are taking place in civilization."

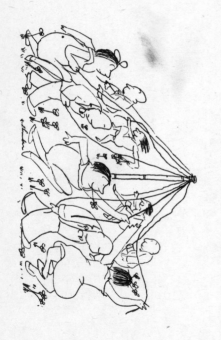

DESTINATIONS

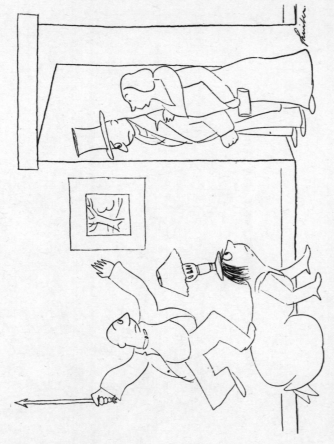

"I don't know them either, dear, but there may be some very simple explanation."

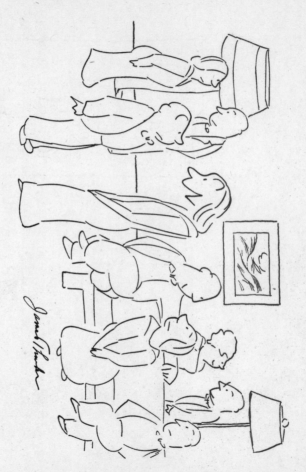

"I love the idea of there being two sexes, don't you?"

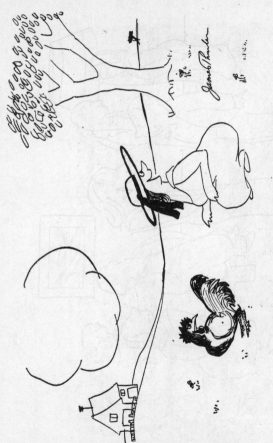

"Yoo-hoo—George! Chanticleer!"

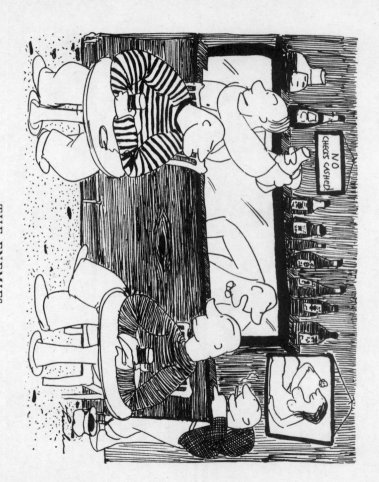

THE ENEMIES

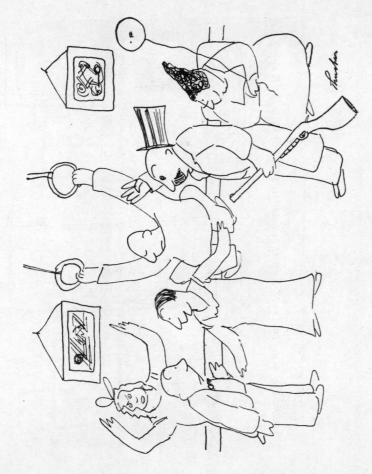

"And *this* is my <u>father</u>, Mr. Williams—home from the wars or something."

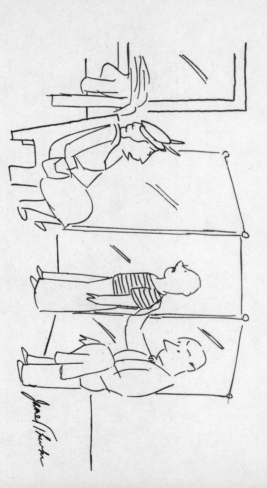

"I don't want him to be comfortable if he's going to look too funny."

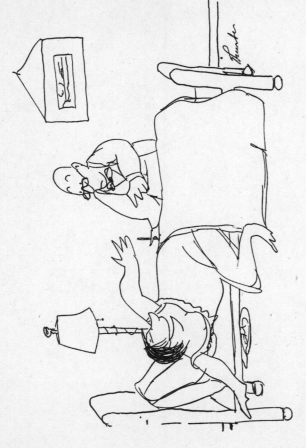

"*I can't __stand__ to have my pulse felt, Doctor!*"

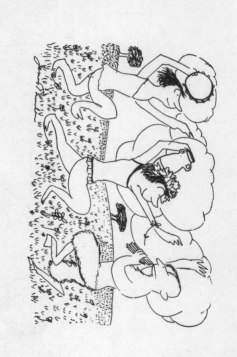

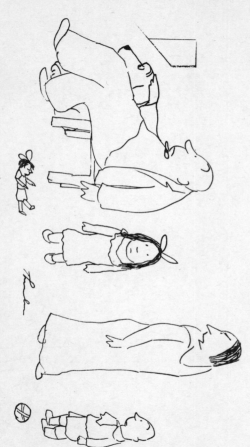

"Well, I'm disenchanted, too. We're _all_ disenchanted."

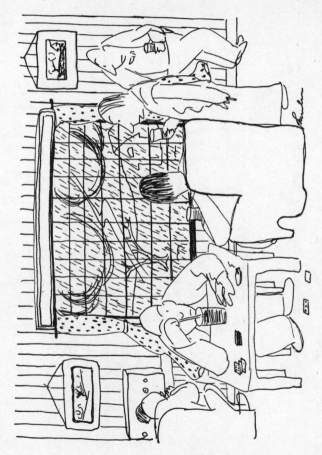

"This is like that awful afternoon we telephoned Mencken."

"You wait here and I'll bring the etchings down."

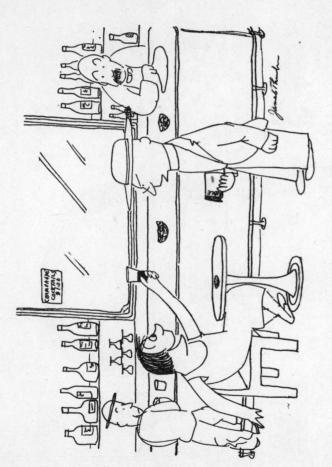

"Unhappy woman!"

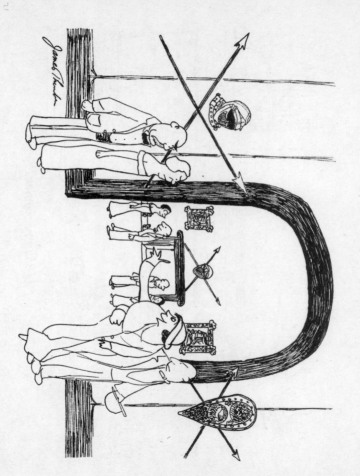

"See you at the barricades, Mr. Whitsonby!"

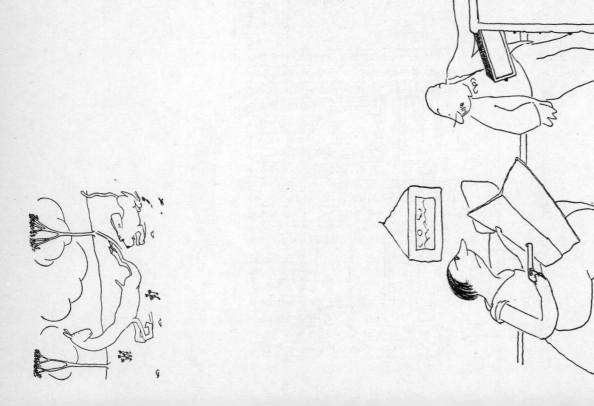

"*Have you seen my pistol, Honey-bun?*"

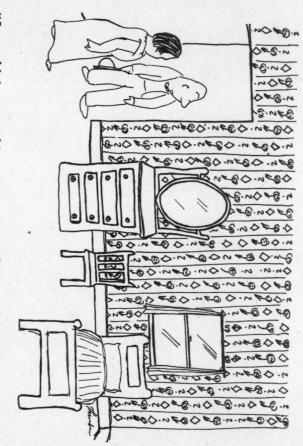

"I wouldn't rent this room to everybody, Mr. Spencer. This is where my husband lost his mind."

"I don't want any part of it."

"I'd dread falling under your spell, Mr. Pierson."

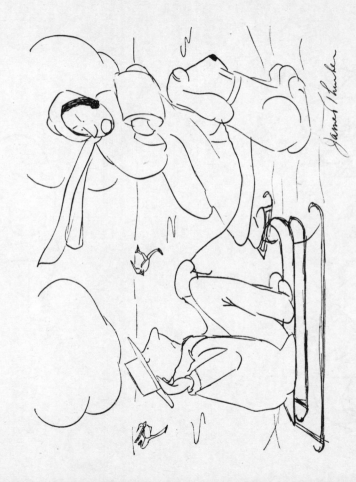

"I said the hounds of Spring are on Winter's traces—but let it pass, let it pass!"

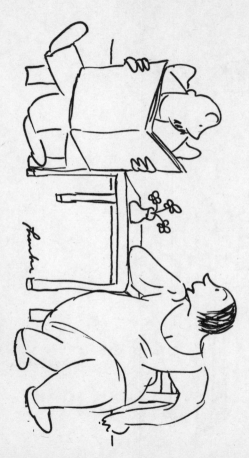

"What ever became of the Socialist Party?"

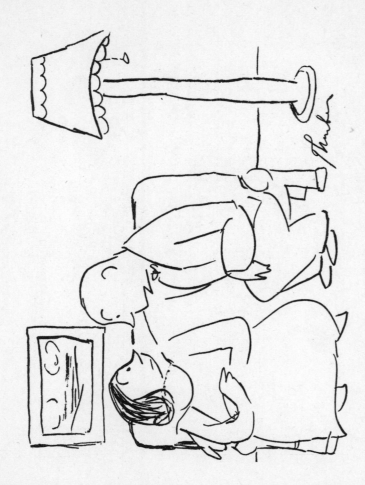

"I wonder what dark flowers grow in the mysterious caverns of your soul."

"I thought you'd enjoy Miss Perrish, darling. She has a constant ringing in _her_ ears, too."

"I brought a couple of midgets—do you mind?"

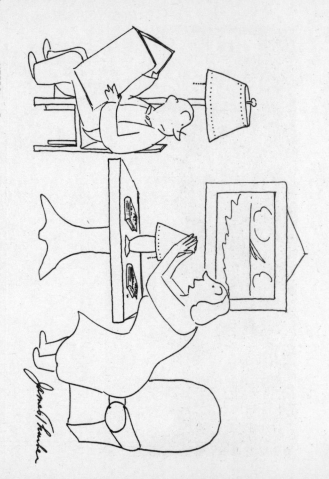

"What do you want me to do with your remains, George?"

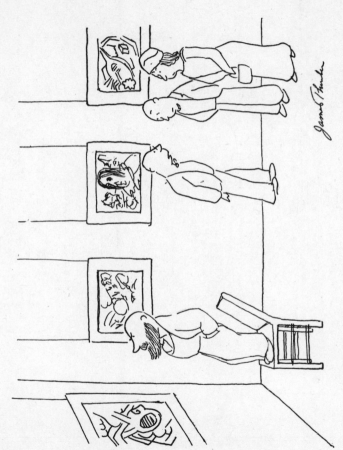

"He knows all about art, but he doesn't know what he likes."

James Thurber

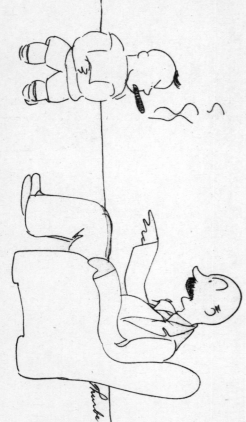

"*Father would be much happier if you wouldn't.*"

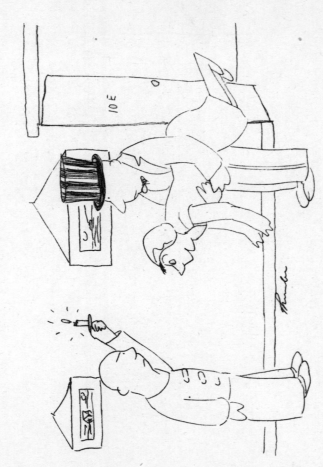

"This gentleman was kind enough to see me home, darling."

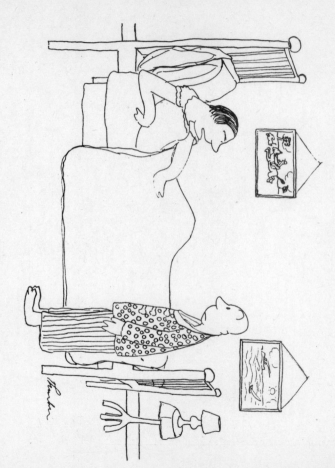

"Well, it makes a difference to _me_!"

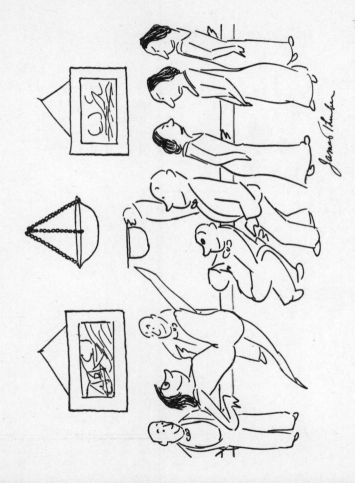

"She's all I know about Bryn Mawr and she's all I have to know."

"It's our *own* story exactly! He bold as a hawk, she soft as the dawn."

"Miss Gorce is in the embalming game."

"Who is this Hitler and what does he want?"

"I beg to differ with you!"

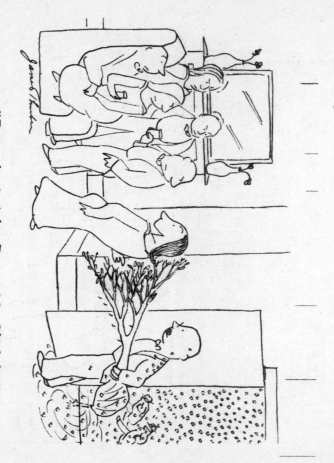

"*Every day is Arbor Day to Mr. Chisholm.*"

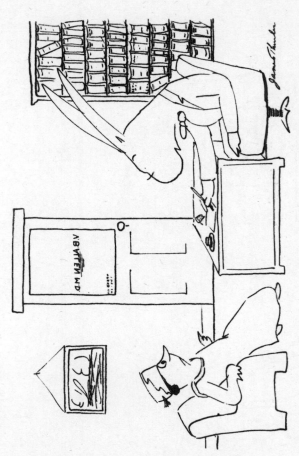

"You said a moment ago that everybody you look at seems to be a rabbit. Now just what do you mean by that, Mrs. Sprague?"

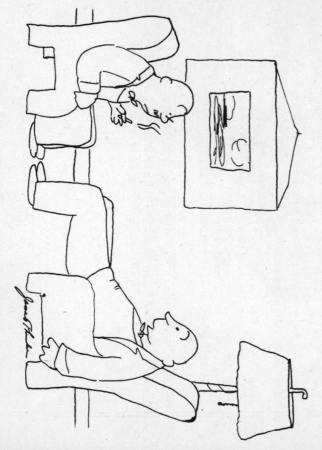

"*I never really rallied after the birth of my first child.*"

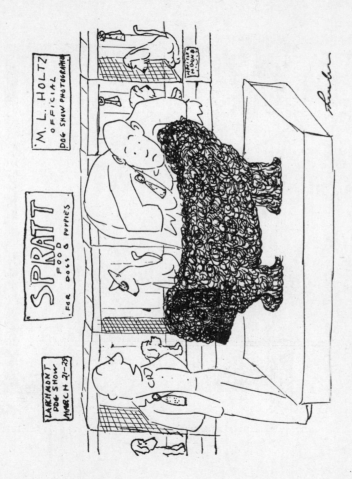

"Other end, Mr. Pemberton."

"Welcome back to the old water hole, Mrs. Bixby!"

"Well, who made the magic go out of our marriage—you or me?"

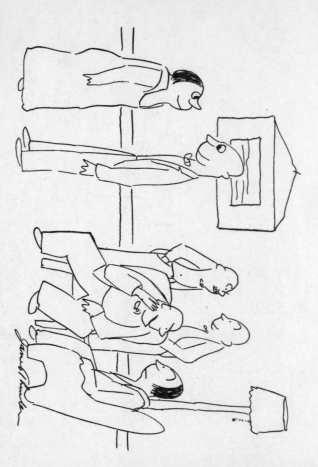

"Le cœur a ses raisons, Mrs. Bence, que la raison ne connaît pas."

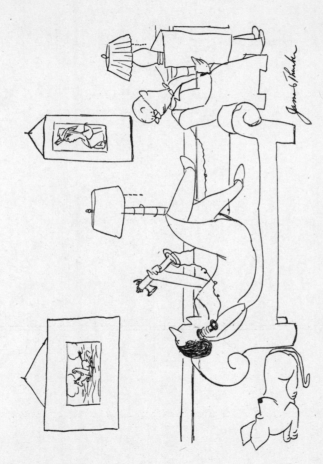

"Well, if I called the wrong number, why did you answer the phone?"

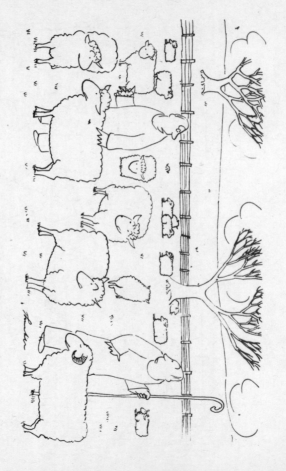

"Would you step over here a second, Waldo? This one's bearing cotton."

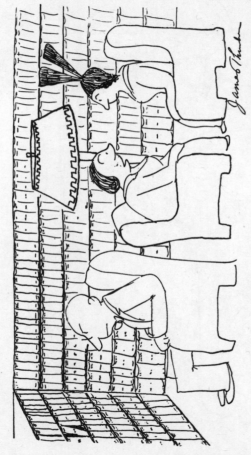

"He doesn't believe a single word he's read in the past ten years."

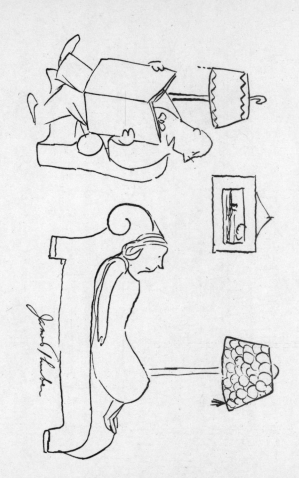

"I do love you. I just don't feel like talking military tactics with you."

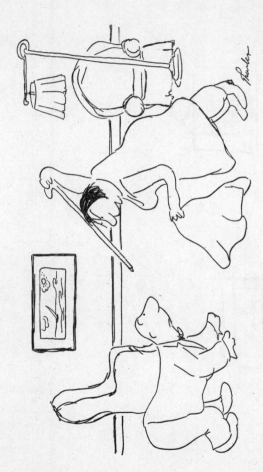

"Now I'm going to go in over your horns!"

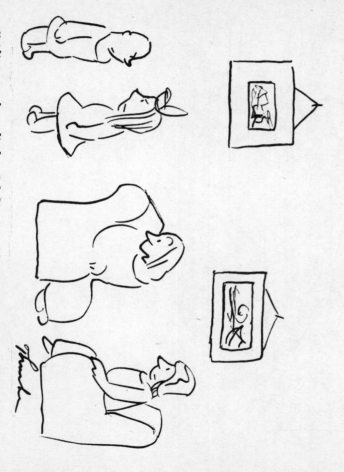

"*Alice can be a little girl Commando in your game, Donald.*"

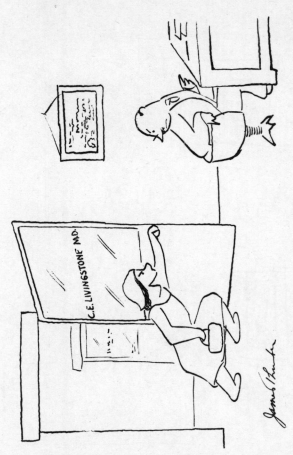

"Dr. Livingstone, I presume?"

"Yoo-hoo, it's me and the ape man."

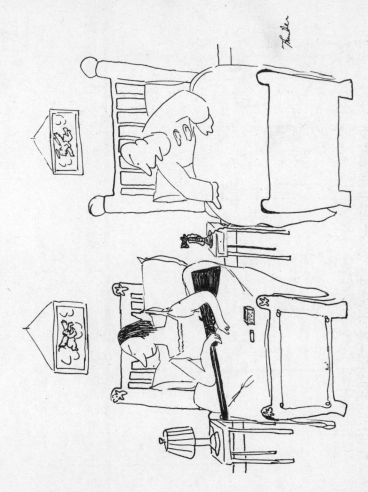

"I tell you there isn't going to _be_ any insurrection."

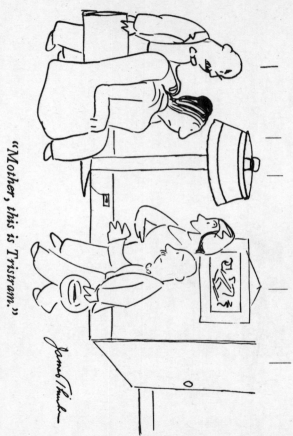

"Mother, this is Tristram."

"*I'm offering you sanctuary, Dr. Mason.*"

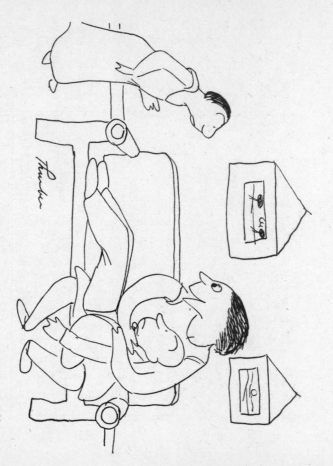

"Your husband has talked about nothing but you, Mrs. Miller."

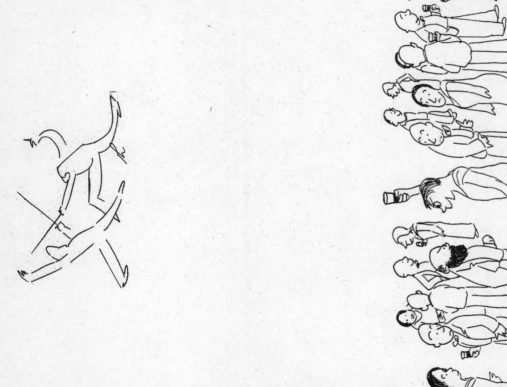

"With a hey-nonny-nonny and a nuts to you!"

119

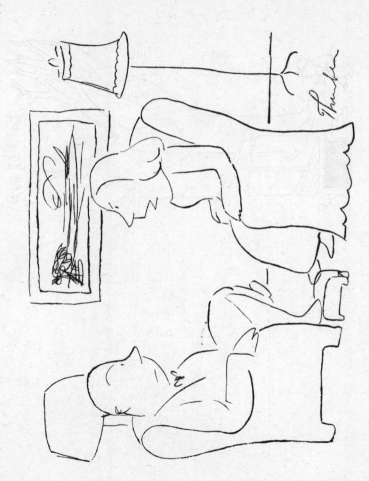

"Which you am I talking to now?"

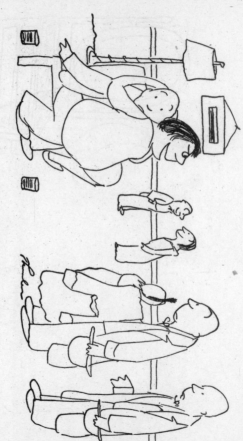

"You can't make me go home!"

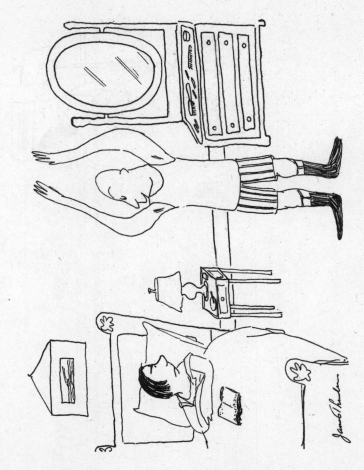

"You can tell me if I bend my knees, Sugar."

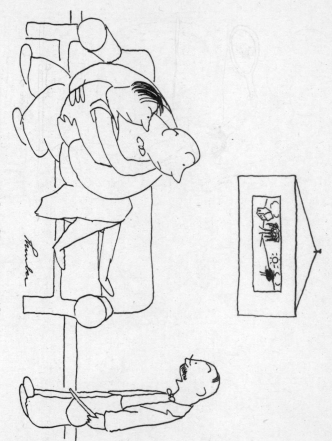

"The party's breaking up, darling."

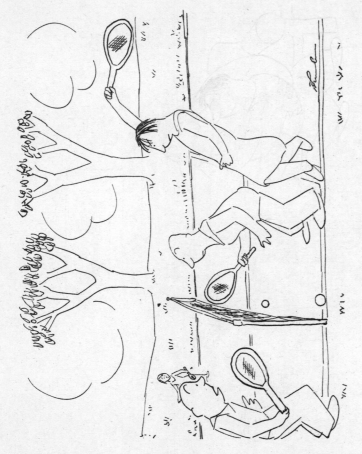

"Look out, Harry!"

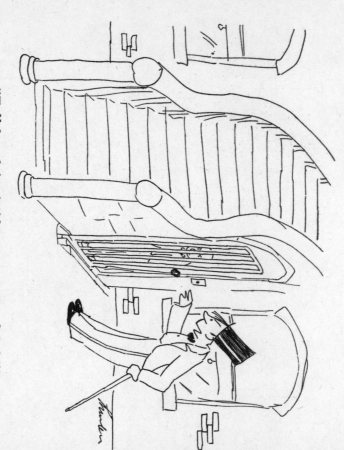

"Tell her she's _afraid_ to come out and fight!"

"This is not the real me you're seeing, Mrs. Clisbie."

"And this is the little woman."

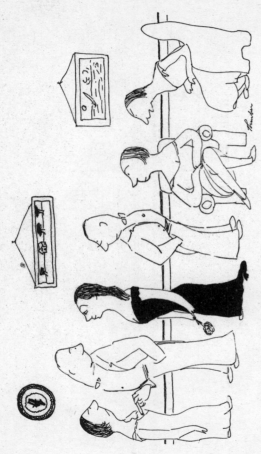

"She's been this way ever since she saw 'Camille.'"

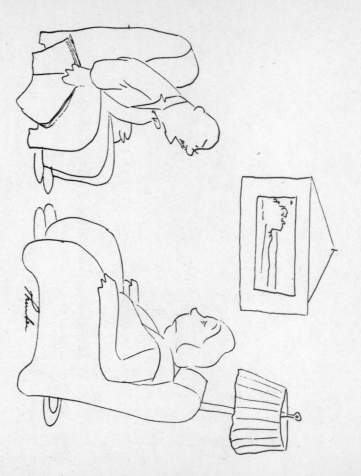

"I assume then, that you regard yourself as omniscient. If I am wrong, correct me!"

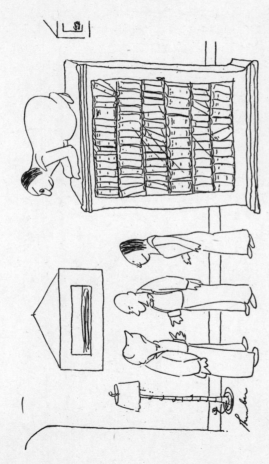

"That's my first wife up there, and this is the present Mrs. Harris."

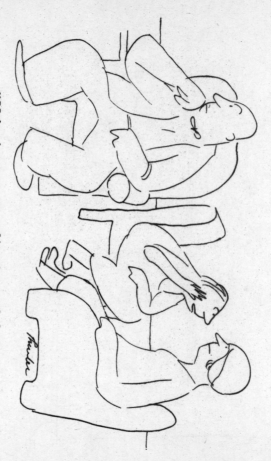

"He's given up everything for a whole year."

"George! If that's you I'll never forgive you!"

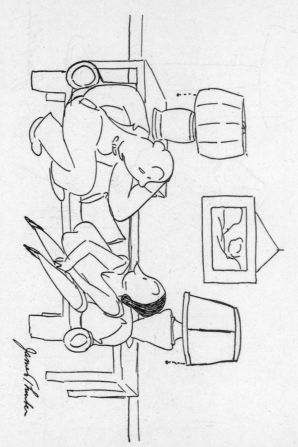

"My wife wants to spend Halloween with her first husband."

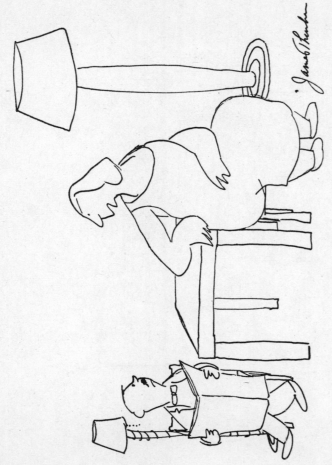

"My analyst is crazy to meet you, darling."

"*She predicts either war or the end of the world in October.*"

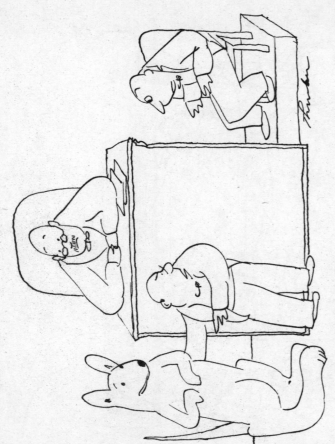

"*Perhaps this will refresh your memory.*"

"Why, Mr. Spears, how cute you look!"

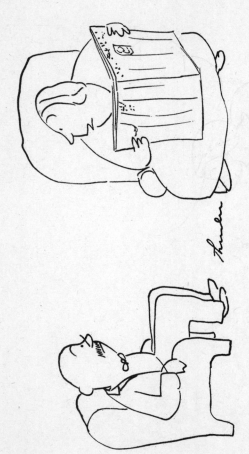

Thurber

"*Lippmann scares me this morning.*"

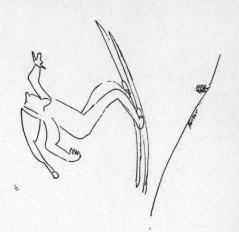

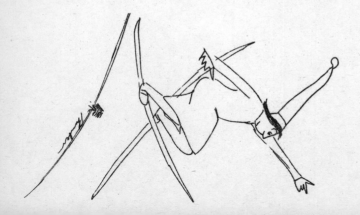

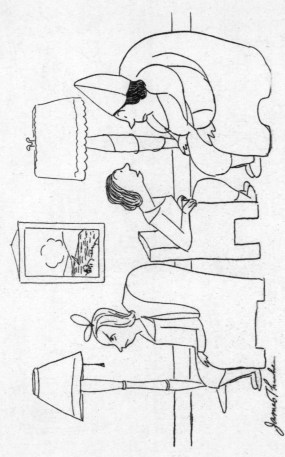

"She says she's burning with a hard, gemlike flame. It's something they learn in school, I think."

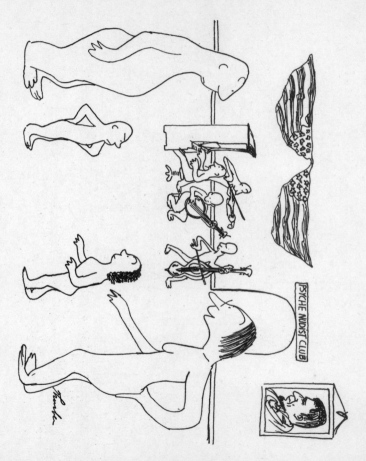

"Dance with the nice man's little boy, dear."

"He's so charming it gives you the creeps."

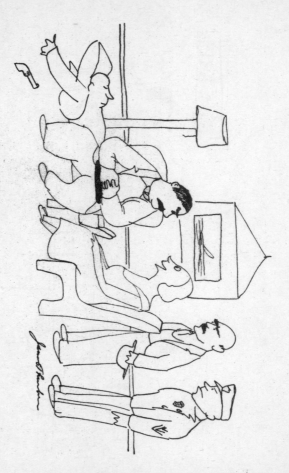

"Well, you see, the story _really_ goes back to when I was a teensy-weensy little girl."

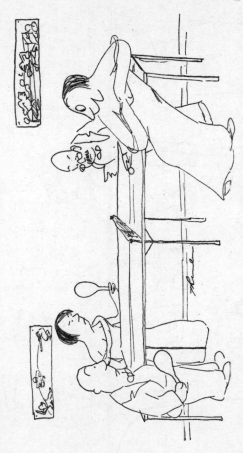

"Do you people mind if I take off some of these hot clothes?"

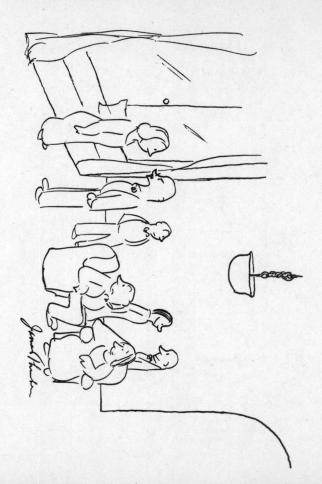

"Will you please cease calling me Sweetie Pie in public?"

"It goes, 'Build thee some stately mansions, O my soul.'"

"Lots of little men have got somewhere—Napoleon, Dollfuss, Billy Rose."

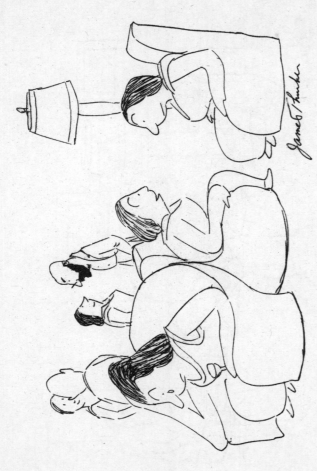

"She's broken up about this play she saw. Thomas Jefferson loses
his wife and four children and Monticello."

"Hello, darling—woolgathering?"

"He doesn't know anything except facts."

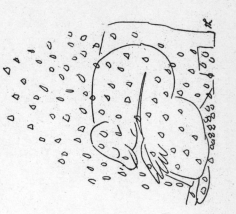

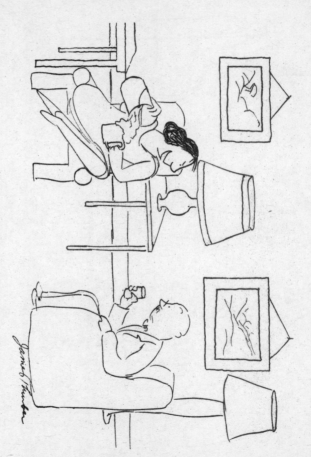

"Laissez faire and let laissez faire is what I believe in."

"Why, I never dreamed your union had been blessed with issue!"

"She built up her personality but she's undermined her character."

"He hates people."

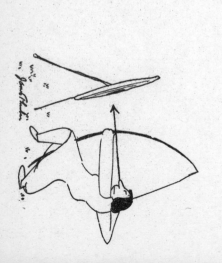

155

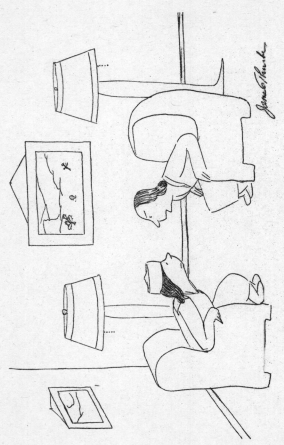

"I say she used to be no better than she ought to be, but she is now."

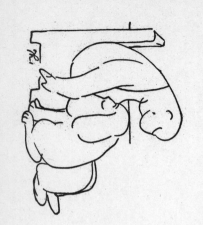

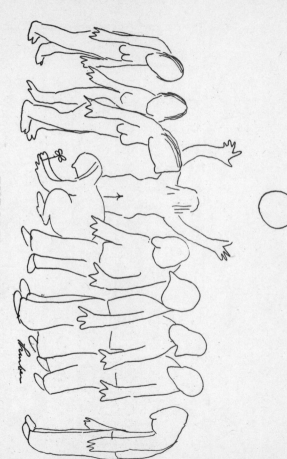

THE LAST FLOWER

"TOBACCO ROAD"

Sundown at the Lesters' house in the grotesquely humorous play at the Forty-eighth Street Theatre, as felt rather than seen by our artist. The characters' souls, or what passes for them, rather than their outward likenesses, are presented here. The bundle of rags on the horizon is Grandma Lester, if not really Patricia Quinn, who plays the part. The other symbols, from right to left, are Margaret Wycherly, Henry Hull, Dean Jagger, Sam Byrd, Reneice Rehan, and Ruth Hunter.

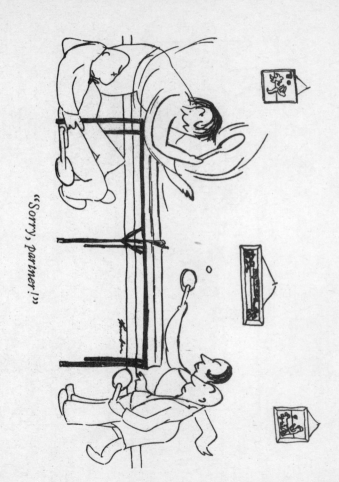

"Sorry, partner!"

"It's Parkins, sir; we're 'aving a bit of a time below stairs."

RAIN IN THE DESERT

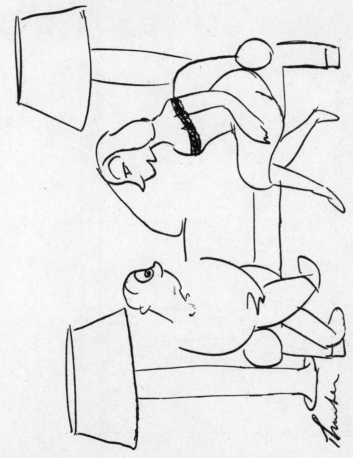

"I suppose all that you men think about is war."

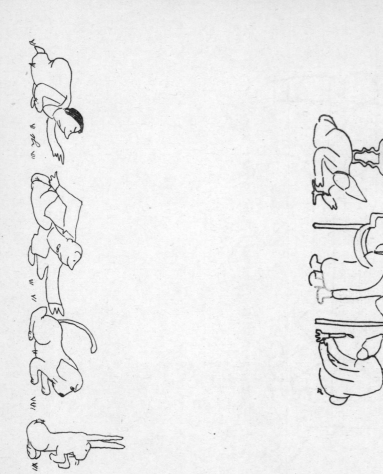

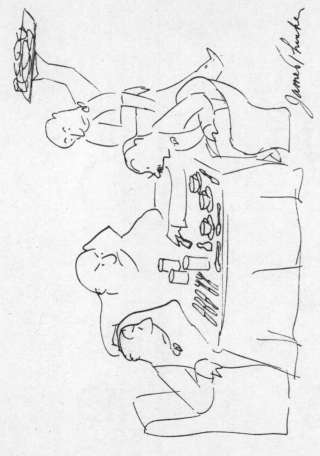

"*Now if I were Oveta Culp Hobby . . .*"

THE HOUND AND THE HAT

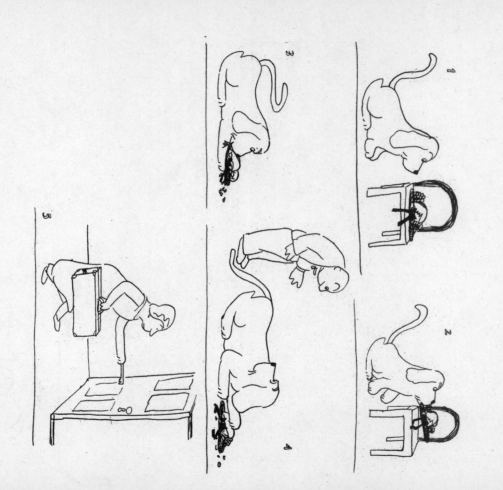

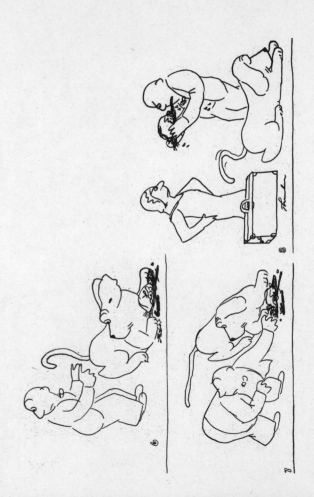

THE MASCULINE APPROACH

The Candy-and-Flowers Campaign

The I'm-Drinking-Myself-to-Death-and-Nobody-Can-Stop-Me Method

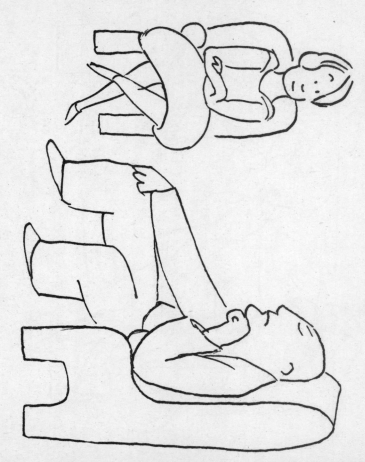

The Strong, Silent System

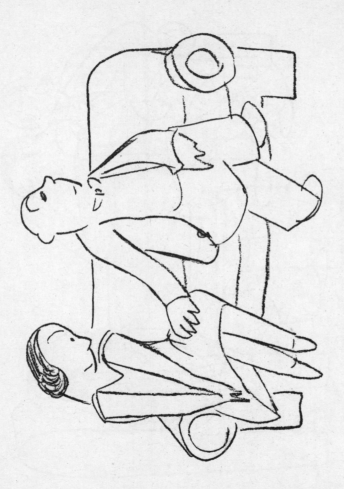

The Pawing System

The Strange-Fascination Technique

The You'll-Never-See-Me-Again Tactics

The Heroic, or Dangers-I-Have-Known, Method

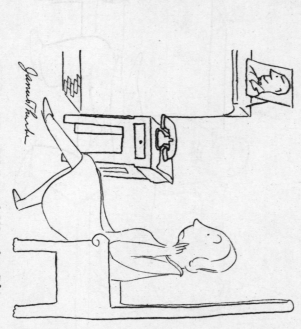

The Let-'Em-Wait-and-Wonder Plan

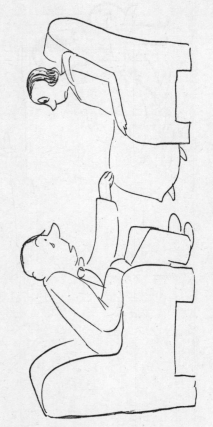

The Unhappy-Childhood Story

The Indifference Attitude

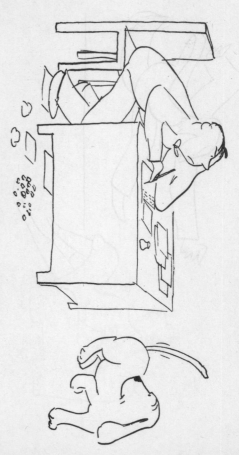

The Letter-Writing Method

The Man-of-the-World, or Ordering-in-French, Maneuver

The Sweep-'Em-Off-Their-Feet Method

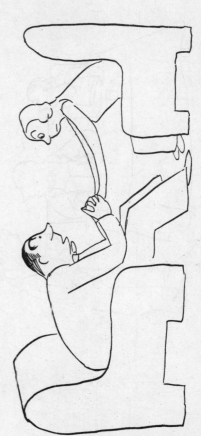

The Her-Two-Little-Hands-in-His-Huge-Ones Pass

The Continental-Manners Technique

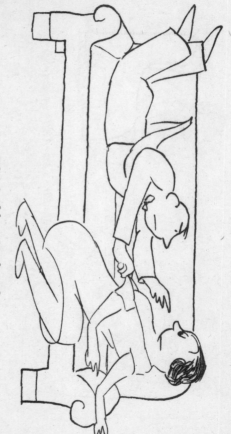

The Sudden Onslaught

The I'm-Not-Good-Enough-for-You Announcement

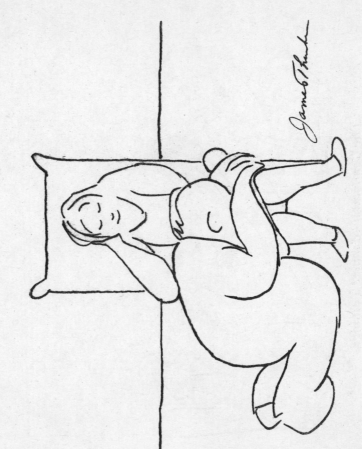

The Just-a-Little-Boy System

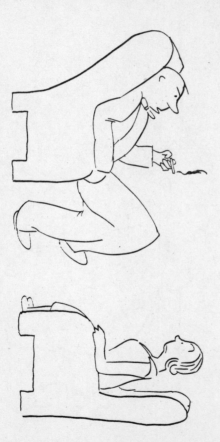

The I-May-Go-Away-for-a-Year-or-Two Move

The Harpo Marx Attack

181

FIRST AID

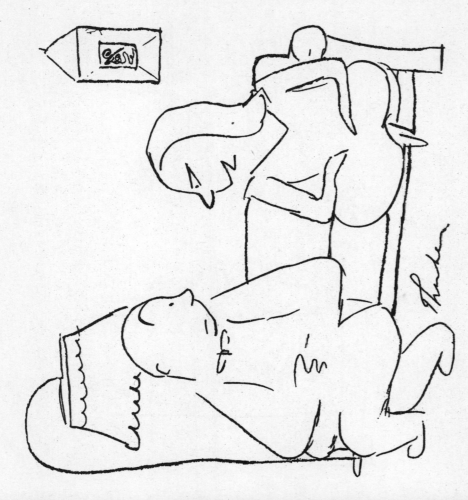

"In first-aid class today we learned eleven different ways to poison people."

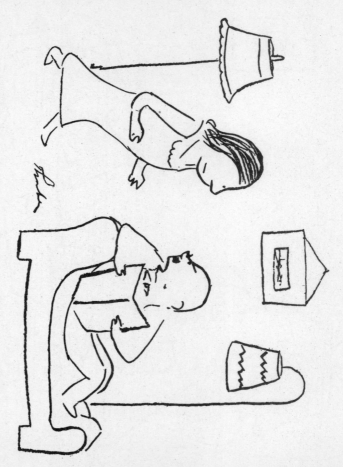

"Well, you're not going to try the fireman's lift on me!"

"I think he's stopped breathing. What do I do now?"

"How's about going somewhere and trying traction splints on each other, Miss Bryson?"

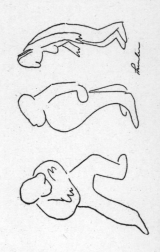

THE WAR BETWEEN MEN AND WOMEN

I. The Overt Act

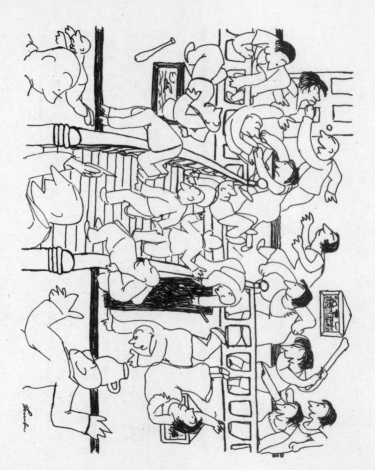

II. *The Battle on the Stairs*

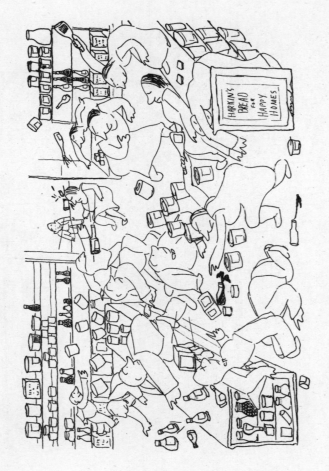

III. *The Fight in the Grocery*

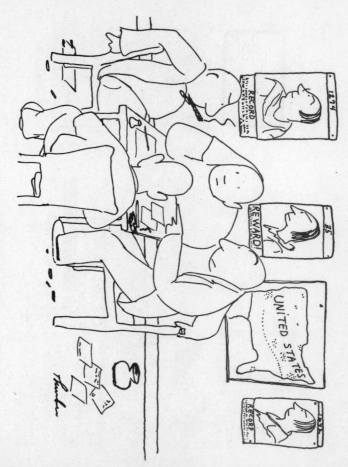

IV. Men's G.H.Q.

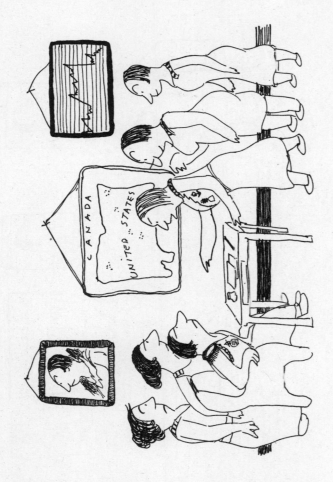

V. Women's G.H.Q.

VI. Capture of three physics professors

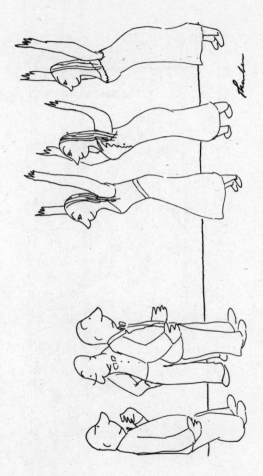

VII. Surrender of three blondes

VIII. *The Battle of Labrador*

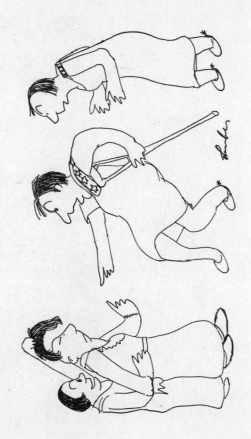

IX. The Spy

X. Mrs. Pritchard's Leap

XI. *Zero Hour—Connecticut*

XII. The Sniper

XIII. Parley

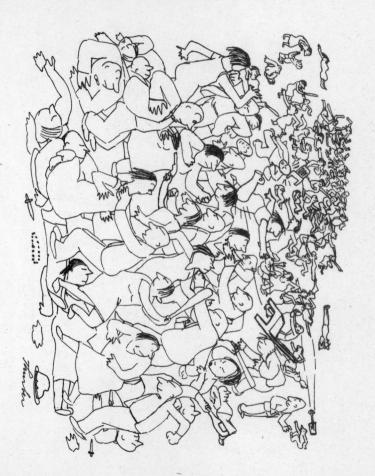

XIV . *Gettysburg*

XV. Retreat

203

XVI. Rout

XVII. *Surrender*

INDEX OF CAPTIONS

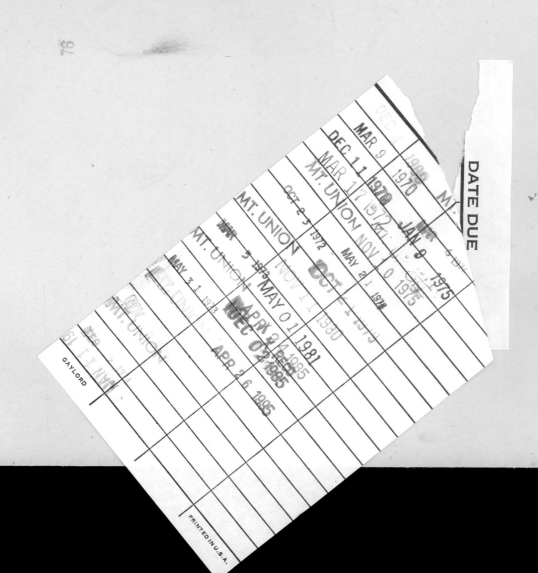

DATE DUE

DEC 1 1969   M.

MAR 9 1969

DEC 11 1970 1970

MAR 17 1972 JAN 9 1975

MT. UNION NOV 1 0 1975

OCT 2 3 1972   MAY 2 1 1975

MT. UNION OCT 2 4 1979

MT. UNION NOV 1 1 1980

MAY 3 1 1978   APR 0 1 1981

MT. UNION DEC 0 1 1985

MT. UNION   APR 2 6 1985

FEB   1

JAN 17 79

GAYLORD   PRINTED IN U.S.A.